Lesley Haskins' fascination with the h
the age of ten when she was taken on a school
Talbot Heath, and she went on to make their history the subject of
her PhD thesis. Carrying out her studies at Furzebrook Research
Station first placed her in contact with the many scientists and
conservationists who, over the years, gave her both the inspiration
and the knowledge to campaign for their protection. This she has
been able to do through the many activities of the Dorset Wildlife
Trust.

Following page
The marsh gentian (*Gentiana pneumonanthe*) does not always
flower at all, and may be easily overlooked, but when it does, such
as after a fire, its beauty is breathtaking *(see page 21)*.

DISCOVER DORSET

HEATHLANDS

LESLEY E. HASKINS

THE DOVECOTE PRESS

To my dear departed Mum - who must have known
something when she gave me the middle name Erica.

Cross-leaved heath (*Erica tetralix*).
Nationally common and universal
on Dorset's wet heaths.

Dorset heath (*Erica ciliaris*).
Nationally scarce and local
on Dorset's wet heaths.

The hybrid between the two species is known as *E. watsonii*.

First published in 2003 by The Dovecote Press Ltd
Stanbridge, Wimborne, Dorset BH21 4JD

ISBN 1 904349 01 3

© Lesley E. Haskins 2003

Lesley Haskins has asserted her rights under the Copyright, Designs
and Patent Act 1988 to be identified as author of this work

Series designed by Humphrey Stone

Typeset in Monotype Sabon
Printed and bound in Singapore

A CIP catalogue record for this book is available
from the British Library

1 3 5 7 9 8 6 4 2

CONTENTS

INTRODUCTION

Dorset has many wonderful wildlife habitats to discover. Its remarkably varied geology and soils, its geographic location in central southern England, its mild climate, its meandering rivers and undulating coast, all combine to offer the explorer a lifetime of discovery just within one modestly sized county. I count myself very lucky then to have been born in Dorset – and perhaps especially lucky to have been born in Poole, the town which gives it name to the 'Poole Basin' – for it is there in the south-east of the county that the heathlands are found. And these are surely the gem in Dorset's crown.

The Poole Basin is actually more like a shallow saucer, whose rim is formed by the chalk uplands, and which has been drowned on one side by the sea. This now half-saucer is filled with Tertiary deposits. There is first a narrow outer band of London and Reading Beds but the middle is strongly dominated by Bagshot Beds and, locally in the extreme east, Bracklesham Beds. Both of these comprise yellow and white sands with seams or pockets of clay which lie at, or at variable depths beneath, the surface. Scattered patches of Pleistocene Plateau Gravels, remnants of the gravel terraces of the ancient River Solent may be found above these, while broad deposits of Valley Gravels follow the major river valleys – the Frome, Piddle, Stour and Avon. The latter are redistributed deposits of the former and both consist of angular flints and pebbles.

Overall, then, the bulk of the Poole Basin is dominated by coarse sands, gravels, pebbles and clays – highly inhospitable parent materials, if not the most inhospitable in the country. Nutrients are readily washed or leached through them to be deposited lower down, leaving the vegetation to eke out an existence in the impoverished upper levels. Raw humus sits on the top while below a hard impermeable pan often develops. This strongly acidic infertile soil type is called a podsol. Where the clay seams or lenses are far beneath

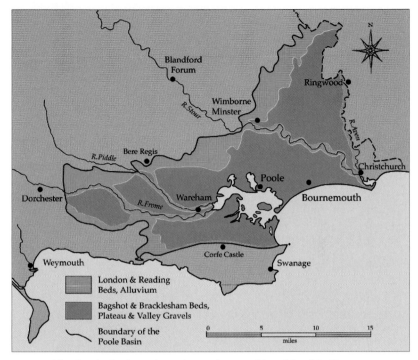

The Poole Basin – the primary home of heathland in Dorset.
The Basin is dominated by Bagshot and Bracklesham Beds
with Plateau and Valley Gravels. These inhospitable sands
and gravels have given rise to very nutrient poor soils on which only
tolerant heathland can easily survive. The marginal London
and Reading Beds and the bisecting alluvium of the river valleys
have richer soils which can support other habitats such as deciduous
woodland and wetlands.

the surface these podsols are deep and freely draining, but where the clay approaches the surface they may be shallow and strongly impeded. The podsols are the soils of the heaths and bogs, with the freely draining podsols supporting dry heaths and the impeded podsols supporting the wet heaths and bog.

Only the alluvial deposits within the confines of the river valleys, and the band of London and Reading Beds round the saucer rim, offer more hospitable parent materials with more fertile soils – and here the heath concedes to other habitats.

Golden Cap is one of the hilltops in west Dorset where heathland has developed on greensands.

Our heathlands in Dorset are representatives of 'European Lowland Heath', a habitat which is restricted to the west European coastal plain extending from southern Sweden through Denmark and north Germany to France and into south and east England. Here they are found on the Cretaceous deposits of the south east, the Breckland, the east Suffolk Sandlings, the east Devon Commons, the Lizard and Land's End Peninsulas and on the Tertiary deposits of the London and Hampshire Basins. The latter area encompasses our own heathlands, as the Poole Basin is actually the natural extension of the London and Hampshire Basins west of the River Avon.

There are, of course, patches of heathy habitat on the Cretaceous greensands and clays capping hills in west Dorset, and even some on the clay deposits of the chalk and limestone downs, but interesting as these might be, it is the heaths of the Poole Basin which comprise the county's true and most absorbing lowland heath.

One is often asked to define heathland. Strictly it is a 'dwarf shrub' community (ie. dominated by plants which are low growing yet woody). Throughout the world there are heathlands dominated by various dwarf shrubs, but for European Lowland Heath the dwarf shrubs are heathers and heaths. Herbaceous and even tall shrub communities may be encompassed within its boundaries on a temporary or permanent basis, but the predominance of heathers is the prime characteristic. It is important to stress at this stage that the extensive tracts of land in upland and western Britain, although also heather clad and superficially like Lowland Heath, are in fact a biologically distinct habitat known as 'Moorland'.

Thus as a representative of European Lowland Heath, the Dorset heaths are representative of a habitat which is scarce on an international and national basis. Moreover, for reasons which will become clear as our discovery of them unfolds, they are arguably the most valued representatives – and amongst the most vulnerable.

THE HISTORICAL HEATH

Would it have ever been possible to persuade John Claridge to see heathland with different eyes? It was he, an itinerant traveller of the eighteenth century who, visiting Dorset in 1793, described our heaths as 'a most dreary waste'. In truth he was experiencing something that many of us would regard as a privilege, namely that of seeing the Dorset heaths in their undiminished glory. His eyes were able to see unbroken purple and golden heathland stretching from his feet to the horizon. His eyes, had he but wished to look, could have seen a wealth of wildlife which we can now only dream about.

Claridge and others bemoaned what they saw as the wild and quite untamed nature of the heath, failing to appreciate that not only was man then having a considerable influence upon it, but that he had been largely responsible for its development in the first place! Examination of pollen preserved in the peat bogs of south-east Dorset shows that in the distant past the vegetation was, just like most of the rest of the British Isles, dominated by woodland – albeit probably a rather lighter cover of woodland than elsewhere, reflecting the naturally inhospitable parent materials and derived soils on which it was growing.

Mesolithic man, even with his simple hunting and gathering activities, seemingly further opened up this light woodland cover, while Bronze Age man had little difficulty in clearing it altogether – and in so doing created the heaths.

This Bronze Age heath formation is evidenced by the sudden increase in heather and grass pollen at the expense of tree pollen preserved in the peat of the local bogs, and by the abundance of

Opposite page:
A round barrow breaks the skyline at Old Knowle, Tadnoll Heath.
Both barrow and heath are the legacy of Bronze Age man.

The heaths were used as rough grazing for cattle, sheep and ponies, as seen here at Arne in about 1900. In 1771 Arthur Young expressed concern that the heaths were overstocked and over-grazed!

heather and grass pollen in the Bronze Age soils preserved beneath round barrows – many of which are to be found on the heaths. Once the trees had been lost and the heath had taken over, the naturally poor soils could only become more so, developing into leached acid and impoverished podsols. This in itself worked to prevent the return of woodland and maintain the dominance of heathland vegetation tolerant of such conditions. In any case man's activities perpetuated the change, as from then on he used and abused the heath for his own ends. As we shall see, the wildlife of the heath developed with, and blossomed under, his rule.

Man put the heaths to a variety of uses. They provided rough low intensity grazing for livestock, including horses (Hardy's 'heath-croppers'), cattle and some sheep (the latter being described by Hutchins in 1774 as a small breed resistant to foot rot or 'coath'). Deliberate small scale burning, to encourage the growth of palatable young heather and grasses, may have been associated with the grazing, at least to some degree. Bracken, or fern, was gathered to provide bedding for the livestock. Heather was cut and used for thatching, broom-making, and as a base for road building. Both burning and cutting took place in the winter.

Dorset is without coal and the region was by then largely devoid of true woodland, so the heath had to provide its inhabitants with fuel – which it did in the form of both turf and peat. Turf was cut from the heath (in alternative squares to promote recovery), while peat was dug from the bogs (in long trenches). 'Turbary' rights carefully defined how much of these fuels could be taken and were fiercely defended. Common gorse, or furze, was also cut, the older stems for fuel and the young shoots for fodder. From under the heath the local people took small quantities of sand and gravel for their needs. Clay, which occurs in localised seams or lenses beneath the heath, was also dug on a small scale. A number of local potteries existed on and around the heaths. The particularly fine-grained 'ball clay' found around Wareham was especially sought after. The requirement of fuel for the potteries and the coastal copperas and alum works sometimes resulted in disputes with the local domestic users.

Attempts were, of course, often made to change the heath into true agricultural land, but the soils were such that the enterprise was normally short-lived, and before too long the land would again become 'covered with furze and ling'.

In the absence of fencing wood or stone, marking boundaries on the heath in relation to these many uses was achieved by the digging of banks and ditches – many of which can still be seen criss-crossing the heathland. The lines of the many cart tracks and tramways which scored the heath as its products were removed are also often evident.

All these activities combined to affect the heath in a number of ways. Firstly the heather and turf cutting and the grazing, (possibly associated with burning), had the vital effect of constantly depleting nutrients so that more demanding non-heathland plants would be prevented from replacing the tolerant heathland ones. Any scrubby vegetation which did establish would, in any case, be removed by these activities. Thus by these means the heath was maintained in its open, largely treeless state. The pulling of bracken kept it in check.

Secondly these activities were constantly 'resetting' parts of the heathland vegetation. Heathland left to its own devices will progress through various phases of growth which ecologists have labelled as pioneer, building, and mature. At any time during this progression, intervention can set it back to the pioneer stage. The activities would have ensured that the heath had representation of all the growth stages

Gorse or furze gathering on Norden Heath, 1899.
Gorse provided a quick fierce flame and was particularly valued for
baking. After the disastrous fire of Wareham in 1724 storage of gorse
within the principal part of the town was forbidden.

– what is now called a 'diverse age structure'. This is significant, since, as we shall see, many elements of the heathland flora and fauna are associated with different stages of the heath. A diverse age structure thus maximises species diversity. The cutting or burning of gorse encouraged it to re-sprout, ensuring a constant supply of rejuvenated gorse on the heath.

Thirdly, and perhaps most interestingly, all the various activities created a whole range of specialised niches which the individual species, both plant and animals, could exploit. As a result of the grazing and poaching by livestock, and the taking and transporting of fuels and minerals, the contours of the heath and bogs were reshaped into irregular forms. Bare ground was constantly exposed – sand and gravel where dry, peat where damp and wet. Ponds and pools were trapped on its pitted surface. In the following chapters we will regularly discover plants and animals making use of all these special habitats, which largely owe their existence to man's exploitation of the heaths.

PLANT COMMUNITIES

As his carriage rolled onwards in quest of more promising terrain, John Claridge apparently only spared a passing glance for the nature of the heath he was crossing. He and other travellers saw only what to them was a monotonous expanse of 'furze, fern and ling'. If only they had looked a little closer! They could have seen a remarkable range of different habitats, changing continuously from one to another depending on the wetness of the terrain and on the uses to which the heath was then being put.

DRY HEATH

The freely draining podsols based on deep sands and gravels support dry heath, the flora of which is delightfully simple. It is normally dominated by the common heather or ling *(Calluna vulgaris)* with its tiny very pale flowers, with a proportion of the more strongly

Western gorse (*Ulex gallii*) seen here, and dwarf gorse (*U. minor*) have separated distribution in Dorset, but occasional plants of western gorse have strayed into the 'territory' of dwarf gorse.

Red threads of parasitic dodder, seen strewn over bell heather.

coloured bell heather *(Erica cinerea)*. The only other faithful component is one of the low growing summer-flowering gorses – and which of the two British species present will depend on exactly where you are. The heaths from Christchurch to Cranborne and from Wareham to Dorchester have the gentle dwarf gorse *(Ulex minor)*, whereas the block of heaths in the middle, around Poole and Bournemouth, have the ferocious western gorse *(Ulex gallii)*. These species have segregated distributions in the British Isles. Western gorse, as its name implies, occuring on the western side, and dwarf gorse on the eastern. Dorset is unusual in having both because their ranges overlap in the mid-south, but this fascinating separation of the two within Dorset has yet to be explained!

Sometimes the heather or gorse will look as though red cotton has been strewn over it. This is the remarkable dodder *(Cuscuta epithymum)*, a parasitic plant which takes its nutrients from its host and, needing no chlorophyll, has red stems supporting its clustered pinkish white flowers. The grass of the dry heath is the small and very fine leaved bristle bent *(Agrostis curtisii)*. Further botanising on the dry heath will provide only a scattering of additional higher plant records. The tiny blue flower of the heath milkwort *(Polygala serpyllifolia)* is well worth searching for and a really careful examination of the sandy exposures of old trackways and mineral workings could reveal the scarce mossy stonecrop *(Crassula tillaea) (see page 51 for illustration)*, the first of the many heathland species to be taking advantage of the special niches created by man. Outside Dorset this little plant occurs only in other heathlands in the New Forest and East Anglia.

It would be quite unfair to leave the dry heath, however, without a mention of the mosses and lichens. The dry heath supports a number of these lower plants and indeed the lichen flora is quite special. These include a number of *Cladonia* species, such as *Cladonia floerkeana*

Dry heath has only a smattering of colourful herbs, including the blue heath milkwort (*Polygala serpyllifolia*) seen here, yellow common tormentil (*Potentilla erecta*), pink lousewort (*Pedicularis sylvatica*), white heath bedstraw (*Galium saxatile*) and heath-spotted orchid (*Dactylorhiza maculata*).

Mosses and lichens are an important and often colourful
component of the dry heathland.

('devil's matches') with its bright red fruiting bodies, which are
particularly in evidence. Bracken, or fern, *(Pteridium aquilinum)* is of
course widespread. Its occurrence is thought to be related to at least a
small degree of soil enrichment.

The proportions of the various species vary with the particular
stage of the heath. After a burn or cut, bristle bent grass makes the
most rapid recovery and bell heather will then become very abundant
before ling finally regains dominance. A search for dodder is most
likely to be sucessful on the younger (pioneer or building) heathland
stages.

HUMID AND WET HEATH

A keen botanist released on the Dorset heathlands is not then likely to
spend too long on the dry heath, but will gravitate quickly to the lower
ground where the water table is naturally high or where a shallow
seam or lens of clay within the sands and gravels has produced an
impeded podsol. For the scientist the crucial indicator of the change to
wet heath will be the appearance of two of the less conspicuous bog
mosses *(Sphagnum compactum* and *S. tenellum)*, but the more visual
change arises from the replacement of the ling and bell heather with

the grey-green foliage of the cross-leaved heath *(Erica tetralix) (see page 4 for illustration)*. At the same time the bristle bent grass is replaced with the larger and wider stemmed purple moor grass *(Molinia caerulea)*. As with the dry heath it is the grassy element which dominates after a fire or cut.

Relatively common on the wet heaths, but special because of its bright yellow splendour, is the bog asphodel *(Narthecium ossifragum)*. Even later in the year the strong orange of its fruiting head adds colour to the wetland. Here the sedges and rushes really come into their own, with deer grass *(Trichophorum cespitosum)*, white beak-sedge *(Rhynchospora alba)* and the many stalked spike rush *(Eleocharis multicaulis)* being certain finds on most sites. The wet heath is also the main home of the carnivorous sundews *(Drosera spp.)*. Dorset can boast all three British sundews since the rarest, the great sundew *(D. anglica)*, occurs on a number of the Dorset heaths *(see illustration*

Bog asphodel (*Nanthecium ossifragum*). *Ossifragum* means 'bone breaker': stock grazing the acid heath were deficient in calcium.

The bog orchid (*Hammarbya paludosa*) is known from a few Dorset sites. Here it grows with the round-leafed sundew (*Drosera rotundifolia*).

on page 24). The sundews are separated by the shape of the leaf, but all have the fine hairs which secrete a sticky substance upon which surprisingly large and unsuspecting insects become trapped and drained of their nutrients; an enterprising way to supplement the diet on these nutrient poor systems!

The wet heath is not only where the botanist will find more plants, but also more of the rare and scarce ones. While the white beak- sedge may be relatively widespread nationally and in Dorset, the brown beaked sedge *(Rhynchospora fusca)* is a much rarer species both inside and outside the county. On the heathlands in and around Purbeck, and rarely just beyond, the cross-leaved heath may be joined by its much rarer cousin, our very own Dorset heath (*Erica ciliaris*) *(see page 4 for illustration)*. This striking, deep coloured heather has a UK distribution which is almost entirely limited to Dorset and the reason for its curious national and Dorset distribution is yet another interesting source of debate.

A close contender for pride of place in the Dorset heathland flora is the marsh gentian *(Gentiana pneumonanthe) (see Frontispiece)*. Its beautiful blue trumpet shaped flowers grace a scattering of our wet heaths in the late summer and early autumn. Although the plant occurs relatively widely on other heaths in the British Isles, the Dorset heaths are the stronghold of this remarkable plant. While it is not certain why marsh gentian occurs on some wet heaths and not others, it is evident that it is one of the several species which likes an open vegetation structure and that its numbers diminish with time after fire and cessation of grazing.

Similarly, but even more so, the rare marsh clubmoss *(Lycopodiella inundata) (see page 51 for illustration)* only occurs when poaching or

Left: White beak-sedge *(Rhynchospora alba)* is one of the several sedges and rushes which flourish in the wet heath.
Right: Brown beak-sedge *(Rhynchospora fusca)* however is a much rarer species both nationally and in Dorset.

For the last thirty years the only population of heath
lobelia (*Lobelia urens*) in Dorset has been at Moreton.

other disturbance provides bare peat for it to establish. It too is very
much dependent upon the Dorset heaths for its national survival and
even here less than 15 sites are now known. The heath lobelia *(Lobelia
urens)* shows similar ephemeral tendencies within its restricted
national distribution and within its now single Dorset location. Add
to this the fact that two of the sundews are most prolific on exposed
peat, and it becomes immediately evident that the more special wet
heathland plants are very much dependent upon bare ground, or at
least an open vegetation structure, which in turn is dependent upon
man's traditional uses of the heath.

There is an intermediate heathland habitat which is still dry enough
to be dominated by ling, but just wet enough to support a good
scattering of cross-leaved heath. It is aptly called humid or damp
heathland and can cover quite extensive areas where the ground
conditions are thus finely balanced.

BOGS, POOLS AND STREAMS

Peat bog, or acid mire, develops in the very wettest of areas where decomposition is so reduced that peat accumulates – often to a considerable depth. Most of the plants of the wet heath also grow here, but the extreme wetness brings in a number of additional and intriguing species.

The essential ingredients are the larger bog mosses *(Sphagnum spp.)*. Their specialised hyaline cells hold water like a sponge and no educational visit to the heath can be complete without a demonstration of how much water can be squeezed out of a handful of bog moss!

The white tufts bobbing over the bog will usually be those of the common cotton grass *(Eriophorum angustifolium)*, but occasionally they will be those of the hare's tail grass *(E. vaginatum)* which, though generally a northern species, does extend its range into parts of Dorset. The bog is also the place to search for a second carnivorous plant, the pale butterwort *(Pinguicula lusitanica)* which like the sundews also uses sticky leaves to trap insects. While the slender white flower of the

White beak-sedge and sundews in a bog on
Stoborough Heath National Nature Reserve.

Some plants use dietary supplements to survive on the nutrient poor heaths. Sundews and butterworts trap insects on their sticky leaves. Bladderworts suck aquatic invertebrates into their tiny bladders.

Top left: The pale butterwort (*Pinguicula lusitanica*) is still present on the heaths, but the common butterwort (*P. vulgaris*) has probably been lost.

Top right: Lesser bladderwort (*Utricularia minor*) is one of the three British bladderwort species found on the Dorset heaths.

Left: The Dorset heaths are home to all three British sundews, of which the great sundew (*Drosera anglica*) is the rarest.

Although written records of peat cutting (as distinct from turf cutting) are rare, the baulks and depressions left from the old cuttings are clear on early air photos, and the oblong shape of some surviving pools suggest this origin – as here on Higher Hyde Heath, near Wareham.

sundew is unfortunately often overlooked, the pale violet-like flower of the butterwort is one of the most memorable sights on the heath. Sadly the stronger coloured flower of the common butterwort (P. *vulgaris*) has not been seen for many a year. But the very special rarity of the bog has to be the bog orchid *(Hammarbya paludosa) (see page 20 for illustration)*. A mainly northern species, this tiny orchid is known from just a handful of sites in Dorset where it finds a home on the open *Sphagnum* carpets. Rarer still, the bog hair grass *(Deschampsia setacea)* is now known from only two locations in Dorset where conditions are both wet and open.

Small streams and ditches frequently drain through and from the bogs while their surfaces and surrounds are often scattered with pools and ponds – most of which have their origin in man's former activities of peat, sand, gravel and clay digging or indeed in his more recent activity of military training! These flowing and still waters provide two further special habitats. Here can be found yet another plant with a carnivorous diet – the aptly named bladderwort *(Utricularia spp.)* whose tiny lidded bladders suck in invertebrates suspended in the water. Like the sundews, Dorset can boast all the British species.

Before moving to the fauna of the heath, special mention must be made of the scrub habitats, not least because they are a key element in supporting the heathland fauna, particularly invertebrates and birds. Common gorse *(Ulex europaeus)* distinguishes itself from the two smaller gorses by growing as a large winter-flowering shrub whose distribution is closely associated with soil disturbance resulting from man's past activities. Old mineral workings and boundary banks are often demarcated by gorse scrub. Left to its own devices gorse eventually becomes open and leggy, but fortunately it responds well to rejuvenation by cutting or burning, to which it was regularly submitted in the past either to provide fuel, or as part of an additonal grazing and burning management regime.

While gorse is the classic shrub of dry heath, that of the wet heath

Stoborough Heath in winter. Common gorse or furze is the shrub of the dry heath providing vital shelter and a well stocked larder for birds – as well as welcome winter colour. With dwarf and western gorse flowering in the summer and autumn, the heath always has a gorse in flower giving rise to the old saying that kissing is in season when gorse is in flower!

Sweet gale or bog myrtle is the shrub of the bog.

and bog is the sweet gale *(Myrica gale)*, so called because of the delightful fragrance it emits when crushed or added to a turf or peat fire.

Pine, birch, willow and broom are further important components of the heathland scrub. However, in recent times at least, all have shown a tendency to exceed their welcome by invading the open heath.

INVERTEBRATES

The heathland invertebrates have fully exploited the whole range of habitats and specialised niches. By rights, of course, the invertebrates should occupy a starring role in any natural history book, but this is particularly the case in this one, as the Dorset heathlands are outstandingly rich in this enormous assortment of creatures.

ANTS

Ants have the privilege of being particularly well studied on the Dorset heaths and the interrelationships of the five black heathland ants, *Tetramorium caespitum, Lasius alienus, L. niger, Formica fusca* and *F. candida* and the three red ones, *Myrmica ruginodis, M. scabrinodis* and *M. sabuleti,* have made a fascinating study. These species not only divide the heath in relation to the dryness or wetness of conditions, but in relation to the stage of the heath. For example *L. niger* uses the wet heath while *L. alienus* and *T. caespitum* both occupy the dry. However *L. alienus* is most abundant in the pioneer dry heath and declines

Ants exploit every type and age of heath in Dorset from the wettest, where the rare black bog ant (*Formica candida*) lives, to the driest.

Left: This spider-hunting wasp stores spiders in its burrow to feed its larvae; whilst (*right*) the rare Purbeck mason wasp (*Pseudepipona herrichii*) stocks its burrows with moth caterpillars.

thereafter, whereas *T. caespitum* does best in the more mature dry heath. Give an ant specialist a sample of ants from an area of heath and he should be able to predict its type and age from the analysis of species present! The ants of the Dorset heaths include rare and scarce species. In particular, the black bog ant *(F. candida)* is found only on bogs in Dorset, the New Forest and Wales, while two species which are parasitic upon *T. caespitum* are also rare. Some other species, such as the black-backed meadow ant (*Formica pratensis*) have probably already become extinct.

BEES AND WASPS

The strongly coloured velvet ant *(Mutilla europaea)* which may be regularly seen on the Dorset heaths, is not in truth an ant at all, but one of the many wasps which live there. The velvet ant lays its eggs on bee grubs in the bees' own nests and the wasp larvae will feed upon them on hatching. However, the true digger wasps actually capture and store various prey for their larvae, often in the security of their specially prepared burrows. The spider-hunting wasps, as the name suggests, specialise in the storage of spiders. One of these, *Homonotus sanguinolentus*, has only ever been known from a few heathlands in Surrey, Hampshire and Dorset and it is encouraging that its presence in Dorset has recently been confirmed. A species with an even more

The green tiger beetle (*Cicindela campestris*) lives in burrows in dry sandy exposures, but may be seen flying in spring and early summer.

restricted range, the Purbeck mason wasp (*Pseudepipona herrichii*), known only from heathlands in Purbeck, stocks its burrows with moth caterpillars. But such creatures may themselves become victims. The mottled bee fly (*Thyridanthrax fenestratus*), whose range extends across the southern heaths, parasitises the sand wasp (*Ammophila pubescens*) while the heath bee fly (*Bombylius minor*), which has contracted its southern heath range to just a few sites in Dorset, parasitises burrowing bees. The mining bees are also well represented on the heathland. The availability of warm open sand, usually as a result of the many forms of ground disturbances created by man's former use of it, is a vital factor in rendering the Dorset heathlands so rich in these fascinating, and often rare, excavating invertebrates.

Heather and bumble bees are almost synonymous, and indeed the heaths are rich in these species which, in some cases, have to bite their way into the bases of flowers, leaving a tell-tale hole behind.

BEETLES

Beetles, including the tiger beetles and the weevils, are numerous on the heathlands. The green tiger beetle (*Cicindela campestris*) and the very rare wood or heath tiger beetle (*C. sylvatica*), like the excavating bees and wasps, need those dry sandy exposures for burrow making. By contrast the beautiful *Carabus nitens*, which occurs primarily on the heaths of Dorset and the New Forest, has a preference for the wet

The raft spider (*Dolomedes fimbriatus*) detects the movements of prey struggling on the water surface of its aquatic 'web'.

heaths. Weevils occur in all the habitats and many are particularly associated with scrub. Scrub is actually rich in many invertebrates, making it a valued component of the heath in its own right and a key element in the food chain.

SPIDERS

There are more species of spider on Dorset heathland than on any other habitat in Britain, exploiting every possible niche from the dry sandy heath to the water of the bog pools. Several are true heathland specialists and exceedingly rare. For *Altella lucida* and *Eresus cinnaberinus* (formerly *niger*) the single dry heathland locations in Dorset are also the only sites for the species in the country. *Alopecosa fabrilis* has the security of one other site in Surrey, while *Cheiracanthium pennyi* is rather more abundant there, but otherwise has only one other site – in Dorset. *Ero aphana* and *Haplodrassus umbratilis* both have their strongholds in the New Forest and less than half a dozen heathland sites in east Dorset. In contrast to these mainly dry heathland species *Zora armillata* occurs on two bogs in Dorset –

The rattling stridulation of the heath grasshopper
(*Chorthippus vagans*) can be heard over dry ground.

and a few fens in East Anglia. Of these great rarities only *Eresus cinnaberinus* is obliging enough to have a common name – the ladybird spider – reflecting the vividly spotted abdomen of the male (*see page 57 for illustration*).

Species which a casual visitor to the heath might reasonably hope to encounter and readily recognize include *Araneus quadratus* displaying its four spotted abdomen in assorted colourways, *Agroeca proxima* leaving its distinctive white egg sacks hanging from the heather, *Atypus affinis* lurking in the vortex of its funnelled web, and the raft spider (*Dolomedes fimbriatus*) poised at the edge of bog pools waiting for potential prey.

GRASSHOPPERS AND CRICKETS

On a summer's day the heath veritably buzzes with the sound of grasshoppers and crickets. Many will also be found in other Dorset habitats, but they include three which can claim to be heathland faithfuls, and, of these, two are national rarities while the third is at least scarce.

The heath grasshopper *(Chorthippus vagans)* is virtually restricted to the heaths of Dorset and the New Forest. Its habitat requirements are not well understood, but certainly it is a creature of the dry heath possibly associated with dwarf gorse. At the opposite extreme of the habitat range, the large marsh grasshopper *(Stethophyma grossum)* definitely likes the very wettest areas – seemingly associated with

The distinctive popping stridulation from the spectacular large marsh grasshopper (*Stethophyma grossum*) can be heard over certain sphagnum bogs.

carpets of *sphagnum* in the valley bogs. Its distribution is only a little wider than that of the heath grasshopper.

But the cricket which typifies the heath must be the bog bush cricket *(Metrioptera brachyptera)*. Although very much a heathland species it is happily unparticular within it, occurring widely over both dry and wet heathland habitats.

DRAGONFLIES AND DAMSELFLIES

For both dragonflies and damselflies the Dorset heathlands are undoubtedly one of the richest habitats in the country. This is a reflection of Dorset's southern location and warm climate, the tolerance shown by many British species to acidic conditions, and the number and variety of essential breeding sites on and around the heathlands. The tiny sphagnum flushes of the bogs are enough for some. Others use the flowing waters of the streams and ditches. Many have readily taken advantage of the still waters of the numerous pools, ponds and lakes created by man's activities – peat cutting, small-scale mineral winning etc. Thus, here again, the use and abuse by man has contributed to the special wealth of wildlife that we are so fortunate to find today.

There are some half a dozen species which are particularly strongly tied to the heathland. The small red damselfly *(Ceriagrion tenellum)* is perhaps most strongly linked, breeding in the small sphagnum flushes. It is rare on a national basis, being confined to the heathlands of

The ponds, pools and ditches are breeding sites for many dragonflies and damselflies. Over half of the British dragonfly and damselfly species can be found on the Dorset heathlands. The rare small red damselfly (Ceriagrion tenellum) needs only tiny flushes in the wet heaths and bogs.

Dorset, Hampshire, Surrey and Sussex. By contrast the black darter *(Sympetrum danae)* is nationally widespread, being associated with both upland moorland and lowland heathland. It is the most common species to be seen on the heathlands in the autumn – but rarely beyond them. Similarly the common hawker *(Aeshna juncea)* and keeled skimmer *(Orthetrum coerulescens)* are relatively widespread nationally but closely linked with the heaths in Dorset. The heathlands are also the place to see the downy emerald *(Cordulia aenea)*, but the ponds which they utilise must be sheltered by trees or scrub. Finally special mention should be made of the southern damselfly *(Coenagrion mercuriale)* and scarce blue-tailed damselfly *(Ischnura pumilio)*, both national rarities whose specialised habitat requirements are met at several sites on the Dorset heathlands.

BUTTERFLIES AND MOTHS

The one group the heathlands cannot claim to be rich in is the butterflies! No matter because the one butterfly which is very strongly associated with heathland, and is particularly well represented in Dorset, has interest enough for many. The beautiful silver-studded blue *(Plebejus argus)*, like its more famous cousin, the large blue *(Maculinea arion)*, has a complex and fascinating life style. The butterfly larvae initially feed upon young heathers and gorses but are later actually taken into the nests of one of the black heathland ants, either *Lasius alienus* or *L. niger*. The pupae are buried in ant cells and the ants have been observed attending the adults until they take flight – over relatively short distances only. Not surprisingly the colonies of the silver-studded blue are very localised and their strong association with immature dry to wet heathland reflects the related requirements of both butterfly and ant. This butterfly is able to exploit similar conditions on a few calcareous grasslands in Dorset and is a special feature of the limestone grasslands of Portland.

While the silver-studded blue may be our very special heathland species, two other butterflies cannot be ignored. Walking along a dry heathland path in summer will almost certainly be rewarded by an easy introduction to the grayling *(Hipparchia semele)*. This large butterfly will sit on the open ground where its grey mottling and careful angling to the sun, to minimise its shadow, will render it

The silver–studded blue butterfly (*Plebejus argus*) has a fascinating relationship with ants. Its colonies tend to be discrete and sedentary and located on immature damp and wet heath.

The grayling (*Hipparchia semele*) loves the dry sandy heath.

virtually invisible. As you approach it will unexpectedly rise up, only to settle again a few paces further on. No other butterfly will offer so many easy chances for a good view! In late spring the heathland also offers the ready prospect of seeing our only green butterfly, the green hairstreak *(Callophrys rubi)*, as its larvae feed on gorse and broom – further evidence of the value of scrub for invertebrate life.

The relative paucity of heathland butterflies is compensated for by the moths. Daytime observation will be rewarded by sightings of the common heath *(Ematurga atomaria)*, the foxmoth *(Macrothylacia rubi)* and the males of the emperor moth *(Saturnia pavonia)*, but the effort of light-trapping will reveal the abundance of the night flying ling pug *(Erpithecia goossensiata)*, narrow-winged pug *(E. nanata)*, yellow underwing *(Anarta myrtilli)* and the true-lovers knot *(Lychophotia porphyrea)* amongst many others. One night's light trapping at Higher Hyde Heath in July produced no less than 194 different species! The speckled footman *(Coscinia cribraria)* was first discovered in Dorset and subsequent records have revealed it to be very much confined to our heathlands and those of the New Forest. However, it has not been recorded in the latter area for some time, leaving it dependent upon Dorset for its survival. Its caterpillars are

Green hairstreak (*Callophrys rubi*) occurs in many habitats, including heathlands, where males may be spotted perched on prominent shrubs in the sunshine.

believed to feed on bristle bent grass implying that pioneer heath may be important to this moth.

Of the many micro moths found on heathland a small space must be reserved for the remarkable bag worm *(Pachythelia villosella),* whose females never leave the caddis fly-like cases which they construct from heather litter.

The rare speckled footman moth (*Coscinia cribrari*) was first identified around 1820 on Parley Common.

REPTILES AND AMPHIBIANS

Those in search of the most famous occupant of Dorset heathland – surely the sand lizard *(Lacerta agilis)* – will head for dry heath, especially where old mineral workings, boundary banks, or other disturbances have left an uneven terrain with open sand. The coastal zone, where heath merges into sand dunes, also meets the lizard's needs particularly well. It is of course the open sand requirement from which the sand lizard takes it name. After emerging from its burrow in spring the male turns bright green to attract the female *(see illustration on back cover)*, who then lays and buries her eggs in the exposed sand. South facing slopes where the warmth will assist incubation are favoured. These sunny sandy prospects may result from the natural lie of the land, but often are caused by past disturbance by man. The sand lizard too has benefited from the many former uses to which the heath was put. Because such habitat requirements tend to be localised, and because their home ranges are modest in extent, sand lizards are often described as occurring in 'colonies'. The young lizards hatch around September and disperse into the surrounding heather to feed on assorted invertebrates before they go, a little after the adults, into winter hibernation. Sand lizards are distinguished from common lizards *(Lacerta vivipara)* by their larger size, stouter outline and bold back markings – individuals can even be identified from their unique patterning.

Smooth snakes *(Coronella austriaca) (see page 50 for illustration)* have much larger home ranges than sand lizards, and do not have the open sand requirement, giving birth to live young. Sand lizards have the helpful habit of basking at the sides of tracks or clearings where they may be relatively easy to see – especially the males in spring. Few of us, however, will see the secretive smooth snake in the wild and must be consoled by the fact that they are relatively unremarkable – a brown/grey body with darker splodges down the sides, quite different

Only about 10% of juvenile sand lizards (*Lacerta agilis*), such as the one here, survive their first year.

from the boldly marked adder *(Vipera berus)* or the yellow-collared grass snake *(Natrix natrix)*. Since each of these reptiles, and the slow worm *(Anguis fragilis),* occur on the heathlands of Dorset, the habitat has the special attribute of supporting all our native reptiles.

It probably appears to the road or house builder that sand lizards and smooth snakes occupy every acre of Dorset heathland. Luckily they are indeed still surviving, against considerable odds, on most of the Dorset heathlands where their special needs are met. However, they are both exceedingly rare outside of the county. It is estimated that Dorset supports 80% of the national population of sand lizards, with only modest populations occurring on some heathlands to the east and a single separate population just surviving on the sand dunes

The sand lizard, as the name suggests, is dependent upon open
sunny sand for breeding.

of Lancashire. Similarly the Dorset smooth snake population
represents about 90% of the UK total. There is just a touch of irony
in knowing that the diet of the smooth snake includes the sand lizard!

The Dorset heaths are actually not a particularly good habitat for
amphibians. Although the waters they require for breeding are
abundant, by virtue of the assortment of former land-uses, the
majority are quite strongly acidic. Only the palmate newt *(Trituris
helveticus)* seemingly favours acid waters, and is consequently the
most commonly occurring amphibian of the heathlands.

The very rare natterjack toad *(Bufo calamita) (see page 66 for
illustration)* did once breed naturally in Dorset, although probably
never extensively. Like the sand lizard it favours both heathland and
coastal dunes, and does still survive in these habitats in several other
counties. Although lost from Dorset for a time the toad has now been
successfully re-introduced to two sites: one of which is one of the few
Dorset sites in which it was definitely recorded in the past.

BIRDS

The special birds of the Dorset heathland are special indeed, not just because they are so rare, but because they are individualists with highly distinctive characters and life styles.

A frustrated road supporter was once heard to protest that Dartford warblers turned up at every public inquiry he had ever been to! The image evoked of this pert little bird purposefully straying from the heath to defend its own cause provoked much amusement. In fact, of all the heathland birds, the Dartford warbler *(Sylvia undata)* is most tightly tied to its heathland home, ideally a stand of thick bushy gorse in the midst of matured, mainly dry, heath. The gorse thicket provides

The Dartford warbler, (*Sylvia undata*) unlike the other British warblers, braves our winters – sometimes with disastrous consequences. The snows of the early 1960s decimated its Dorset population. Hot summers are also a problem. The extensive fires of 1976 caused the recovered population to crash again.

a secluded summer breeding site, from which can occasionally be heard the bird's plaintive, distinctive, mewing call. The gorse also provides a good source of its exclusively invertebrate diet. In a bad winter, when the surrounding heather may be snow-covered and thus unavailable for foraging, the shelter and snow-free larder that bushy gorse provides is thought to be vital to the bird's survival. Harsh winter weather is certainly one of the major factors controlling population numbers. Another is large scale fires, when all available gorse may be uniformly burnt back to ground level. However, rejuvenation of gorse is essential to the Dartford warbler, for once old and leggy, gorse provides little shelter and food. In the past this regeneration was achieved by cutting gorse for fuel and possibly as a result of the controlled burns associated with heathland grazing. Thus the Dartford warbler has doubly benefited from man's activities – initially from the ground disturbance which first encouraged gorse to establish, and subsequently from the treatment of it which ensured suitable bushy growth on a cyclical basis.

While Dartford warblers 'mew', nightjars (*Caprimulgus europaeus*) are said to 'churr'. Unlike the Dartfords, nightjars (*see page 54 for illustration*) are with us only in summer, when an evening walk on the heath is quite likely to be rewarded by hearing this remarkable call, and even a glimpse of the bird in flight. There is no nest as such, just a scrape on the ground – usually in a gap in the heather created by an old tree stump, or a bracken patch where the bird's mottled plumage helps provide camouflage. Feeding, mainly on moths, is concentrated at the beginning and end of the night, when the nightjar may either fly freely with wide mouth agape or conduct short sorties from a chosen perch. Radio tracking of nightjars has shown that they commonly travel beyond the heath, to adjoining wetlands or deciduous woodlands, to feed. Nightjars have particularly benefited from the temporary areas of heathland created as conifer plantations are felled.

Another ground-nester is the woodlark *(Lullula arborea)*. Woodlarks seemingly like a certain amount of older heather for their nest sites in an otherwise rather open mixture of bare ground and young heather. It is not then so surprising that they are known to be particularly successful in several of the heathland sites used by the Ministry of Defence. All three of these birds, being closely linked to

The hobby *(Falco subbuteo)* may return year after year to the
same nest site in old pines above the heath.

heathland, are all very restricted in their UK distributions, so Dorset is
critical in maintaining their numbers nationally. For Dartford warblers
Dorset and Hampshire are *the* critical counties in this respect.

There is nothing to equal the sight of a hobby *(Falco subbuteo)* in
swift and agile pursuit of dragonflies over the heath. Another fair-
weather visitor, it nests in old pines towering above or around the
heath, often making use of old abandoned crows' nests since it does
not build its own. Although the hobby now mostly feeds over the
heath rather than actually breeds upon it, the heathlands of Dorset can
nevertheless also claim a key position in the national success of this
rare and beautiful bird.

We cannot leave the heath without a word for the stonechat
(Saxicola torquata), for although it does occur on other habitats in the
county it is strongly associated with heathland. It also really does have
the helpful habit of cheerfully displaying itself on the tops of the gorse
bushes in which it feeds and breeds – unlike the Dartford warbler
which is only rarely glimpsed in such an exposed position. From here

A colourful stonechat (*Saxicola torquata*) emits its distinctive song from the top of a common gorse bush. Gorse is a vital source of food and shelter not just to the Dartford warbler and stonechat, but also enables many other birds to make a living on the heaths.

its readily identifiable song, just like two stones being knocked together, can be clearly heard. Add to these attributes its colourful markings, and you understand why the stonechat is most people's favourite heathland bird. Common gorse is not, of course, only important to the stonechat and Dartford warbler. Its shelter and rich invertebrate population enables a much greater diversity of birds to use the heath than would otherwise be possible. Rare and common birds alike then owe much to man's disturbance of the heath, which has encouraged the growth of common gorse.

Nor should we fail to recall that the wet heaths and bogs used to be rich breeding grounds for curlew (*Numenius arquata*) and snipe (*Gallinago allinago*). We must be grateful that just a few pairs do still breed on a very few sites. Also that hen harrier (*Circus cyaneus*) and merlin (*Falco columbarius*) choose to roost on and forage over our heaths in the winter months so that our cold weather walks might just be rewarded by a glimpse of these wonderful raptors in place of the long-departed hobby.

THE HEATH IN MODERN TIMES

OUR SPECIAL HEATH

To discover the Dorset heaths and their wildlife is then a very special privilege indeed. While we walk their sandy tracks we are all the time aware that they do not have many counterparts, either in the United Kingdom or even in Europe. And those that there are cannot match the richness and rarity of species which we can see here.

In part this is a function of the geographical location of the county in the middle of southern England. In every plant and animal group we have considered there are those which just extend their natural range here from the west, east, north or south. In part it is a function of the mild and sunny climate of this location which particularly benefits the species we have encountered which thrive in dry hot summers or, like the Dartford warbler, rely on mild winters. In part it is a function of man's use of the heath which has ensured habitat diversity and the abundance of special niches. Many times we have seen how both plant and animal species need this diversity and exploit the niches.

Also very special is the fact that the Dorset heaths offer the opportunity to discover transitions into other habitats – into deciduous woodland and meadows in the river valleys and the margins of the Poole Basin and, even more specially, into brackish grasslands and saltmarsh along the shores of Poole Harbour, nutrient rich flushes below the Purbeck Hills, and into sand dunes on the coast. All these factors then combine to make for a richness and rarity of habitat and species unparalleled by the other United Kingdom heaths.

Unfortunateley, the decline of the Dorset heathlands in modern times has also been unparalleled.

Only thirty years before John Claridge's visit to Dorset at the end of the eighteenth century, Isaac Taylor had produced the first one inch to the mile map of Dorset, showing quite plainly that the vast majority of the Poole Basin was then open heathland broken only by the more fertile soils of the main river valleys and the harbour shores – some 40,000 hectares in all. Yet less than 20 years after Claridge's visit only 30,400 hectares remained. The losses which followed constitute one of the most relentless and dramatic habitat declines ever recorded in this country. Claridge would have been well pleased!

The greatest impact came as the small scale, and often temporary agricultural incursions of the past were replaced by large scale and permanent conversions through the determined application of new and improved agricultural techniques – despite the fact that the resultant farmland was often of marginal productivity.

But not all the heathland was converted to the productive agriculture of which Claridge so particularly approved. In the mid 1700s a few landowners started to experiment with tree planting. The first attempts with deciduous trees failed dismally on the poor soils, but pines were found to have better success. The two most commonly used were the Scots pine *(Pinus sylvestris)* and the maritime pine *(P. maritima),* the latter becoming known locally as the Bournemouth pine. Even so it was not until the formation of the Forestry Commission in 1919 that the loss of heathland to conifers commenced

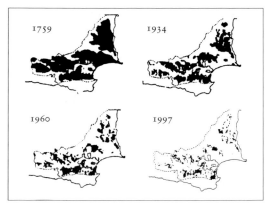

1759   1934   1960   1997

Opposite page: Isaac Taylor's fascinating map, of 1765, the first one inch to the mile map of Dorset, clearly depicts and names large areas of open heathland.

Left: Maps to show the reduction and fragmentation of heathland in the Poole Basin from 1759 to 1997.

in earnest, this time almost exclusively with Scots pine and Corsican pine *(P. nigra)* which, alone amongst the conifers, were deemed to grow well enough to be worth the effort.

Urban development of all types took another major bite. The growth of east Dorset's towns has inevitably had a major impact on the heathlands. Poole and Christchurch expanded from small ports,

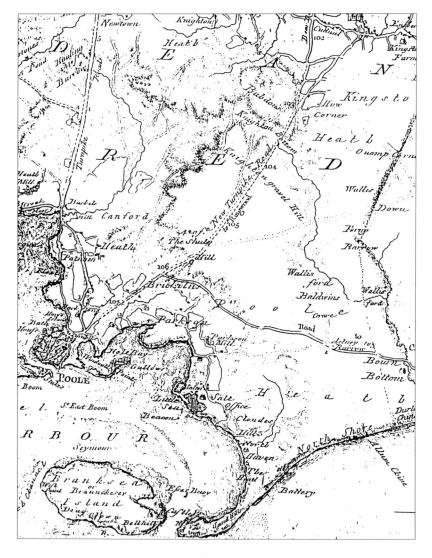

Ornamental Drive, Puddletown, past (1913) and present.
Puddletown Heath was planted with conifers by the Forestry Commission
to become Puddletown Forest. Infestation by Rhododendron consumed
even the surviving roadside heathland.

while Bournemouth mushroomed out of virtually nothing to unite
them and the outlying villages into one of the largest and fastest
growing conurbations in the country. The original heathland is now
only recalled in road names – Turbary Crescent, Bracken Road and
Stonechat Close. Major new roads were required to serve the
developments and both required massive supplies of raw materials.
The sand and gravels which lay under the heath were suddenly in great
demand and the small scale excavations of the past were replaced with
extraction on an entirely different scale, requiring wholesale removal
of the heath above. Similarly the ball clay industry, which had
previously been a largely small scale enterprise, increased the scale of
its operations and its impact on heathland around Wareham. Even as
recently as the late 1970s the new oil industry took its toll as the rail
terminal at Furzebrook was built on heathland. Initially the value of
heathland was not understood and its conversion was widely accepted

as a commendable enterprise. Later the momentum was simply too strong to stop.

As the heathland declined in extent, it also became increasingly fragmented and divided. The maps which document heathland loss also show the progressive division of the original few major blocks into more and more fragments, increasingly separated from each other by other land uses.

Habitat loss and fragmentation has inevitably affected species, especially those with special requirements and low mobility. The

Pound Lane, Poole, past (1926) and present.
Poole Heath, which once stretched from the port to Wimborne, has been almost entirely lost to housing. The sign records that the Longfleet pound for stray animals was located along the lane.

Populations of species have declined along with the heathland. The rare and harmless smooth snake (*Coronella austriaca*) requires sizeable areas of heathland on which to live and its numbers have declined dramatically.

population of sand lizards and smooth snakes declined drastically. The ladybird spider was believed lost for some time, and the natterjack toad was indeed absent until recent re-introduction. Somewhat suprisingly heathland fragments have been found to be comparatively rich in terms of numbers of species present. However, close inspection reveals that this is due to invasion of non-heathland species from surrounding habitats while characteristic heathland species are actually low in number.

DECLINE OF TRADITIONAL USE

As the Dorset heathlands were reduced and fragmented, the traditional uses of the remainder declined. Grazing by domestic stock became less common, eventually rare, leaving only minimal impact by deer, and the pulling of bracken for bedding ceased. The cutting of

Above: Marsh clubmoss (*Lycopodiella inundata*) is one of the several plant species needing bare peat to flourish.
Below: Mossy stonecrop (*Crassula tillaea*) exploits sandy exposures alongside trackways and in old small mineral workings.
Surveys in the early 1990s have shown that both these plants have been largely lost from locations where they were recorded in the 1930s, despite the heathland habitat itself having survived.

heather died out. The arrival of the railways in the mid-nineteenth century made coal available for fuel, so that the gathering of gorse faggots, turf and peat from the heath was no longer required. Those rights, once held so precious, ceased to be exercised. At the same time the small scale digging of sand and gravel for local needs died out. Although the winning of the special ball clays around Wareham continued and increased, the digging of the more ordinary clays for local potteries declined and eventually ceased. In short, the heath was no longer needed for the assortment of uses to which it had so long been put and the wildlife was left to face the consequences.

Firstly, without the cutting of heather and turf, and without the grazing and burning, the soil nutrients were no longer continuously depleted. The consequent build up of nutrients permitted the growth of the more demanding scrub and bracken. Without these activities or the pulling of bracken there was nothing to keep their spread in check. In the decade between 1979 and 1989 the greatest loss of heathland in Dorset was to scrub. The very essence of the heath – its gloriously open landscape – was insidiously changing.

Secondly, the heathland was no longer subject to the constant 'resetting' of the past. It was left instead to turn widely into mature heath with a consequent decline in age and structural diversity. Since, as we have seen, different species are often associated with different ages of the heath, this resulted in a decline of species diversity. Neither was the gorse subject to its rejuvenating cutting or burning, leaving it to become leggy or moribund and unable to perform its key roles for invertebrates or birds.

Thirdly, the creation of the many specialist niches which the various plants and animals had thrived in declined. Without man disturbing the ground through his various activities there was less opportunity for common gorse to newly establish itself or replace those stands dying out. Open dry ground, so essential to many invertebrates, the sand lizard, and some birds and plants, diminished. On the wet heath the several plants requiring the open peat created by poaching by domestic stock lost their essential habitat. With the ending of peat cutting and small scale mineral working, the occurrence of ponds – home of the bladderwort, raft spider and breeding ground for so many dragonflies and damselflies – declined.

As if all this was not enough, another problem arrived from abroad. Rhododendron *(R. ponticum)* was imported from the Balkans to provide cover, where it fared exceedingly well on the acidic heathland. More recently it has been joined by the North American crowberry *(Gaultheria shallon)*. Both species rapidly obliterate the heathland flora and have little to offer our native fauna in return.

Heathland is very vulnerable to trampling even by foot.
When scrambling occurs large bare areas may be created.

In summary, the practices which had kept the heathland open, provided a diverse age structure, and created the special niches for its wildlife, came to an end, while alien and highly invasive species have run amok. The threat which these changes posed was initially overshadowed by the more glaring problem of habitat destruction and fragmentation. However, as the deliberate destruction of the heathland has declined, these important issues have come to the fore and are one of the two major challenges now facing heathland conservation in Dorset.

URBANISATION

Apart from being reduced, fragmented, neglected and invaded by aliens, the heathlands of Dorset have yet another challenge to face! Many now lie in the heart of one of the largest conurbations in the country, and none are any great distance from it. They are accessible to, and actively used by, the public on a significant scale. This can and does have effects upon the habitat and its wildlife.

One of the most fundamental problems arises from the structure of heathers. Being dwarf shrubs they are low growing yet woody and when trampled by foot, hoof or vehicle they readily snap and die. Thus existing paths may be easily widened and new paths created by walkers and horse riders, and when mountain or motor bikes are involved large bare scars are rapidly created. Unfortunately, such

Ground-nesting birds such as the nightjar (*Caprimulgus europaeus*) are easily disturbed by walkers and their dogs. Nightjars have not succeeded in breeding on some of our smaller urban heaths in recent years.

ground cannot provide the niches required by the peat or sand loving species since they are likely to be too regularly disturbed. Indeed, they arguably present a serious hazard to some, particularly the sand lizard, who may be attracted to lay eggs in a position where they could soon be destroyed.

Another problem relates to disturbance of the fauna. Our knowledge of this subject is not as full as it should be, but there can be no doubt that some species are especially at risk. In particular the rare ground-nesting birds, the nightjar and woodlark, are vulnerable to disturbance by humans and by their dogs if either wander from well-established paths. Surveys have shown that the heathlands which are within or close to the conurbation which are subject to regular access by walkers and their dogs support fewer breeding nightjars and woodlarks than their more rural, less used, counterparts. They appear to have disappeared altogether from some urban sites. Nightjars have a further, or possibly greater, problem on urban sites, in that the adjoining habitats which they commonly use for foraging have been largely lost to development.

Dogs introduce a particular problem by enriching the edges of paths which criss-cross the urban heaths with the result that the heathland species are replaced by lush grasses. Reptiles and ground-nesting birds are very vulnerable to predation by cats and rats.

Finally, there is the increased risk of uncontrolled large scale burning which is now an inevitable part of the urban heathland scene, particularly in the spring and summer. We have seen that in the past the heaths were probably deliberately burnt in association with grazing. However, it was small scale, carried out in the winter, outside of the breeding season, under conditions when the burn would have been comparatively light. Moreover it was conducted in an age when the heathlands were much more extensive and united. This traditional practice, therefore, gave the advantages of depleted nutrients, a diverse habitat structure, varied flora and fauna, rejuvenated gorse and so on. At the same time it did not seriously threaten the survival of individual species, as even the less mobile generally had both the opportunity and time to recolonise gradually from the surrounding unburnt heath. Modest, light and infrequent fires have some advantages even today.

Fires are much more common on the urban heaths than the rural ones. Fire does not destroy heath, as commonly stated, for the plant communities generally re-establish, but much damage is done, especially to less mobile animals.

Upton Heath. Like many of the urban heaths Upton was once the subject of a variety of development plans. Now it is protected and appreciated as an asset for wildlife and humans alike.

However, the extensive, frequent, deeply burning spring and summer fires to which our now reduced and fragmented urban heaths are all too often subjected are highly damaging. Large stands of bare and later immature heath replace the varied age structure, and less mobile species, especially the rare reptiles, are severely affected. Their timing maximises impact on the wildlife and its breeding success. Repeated fires over the same area can result in permanent change to grass dominated heath or even bracken or birch scrub.

Undoubtedly then Dorset heathland has faced, and continues to face, significant difficulties. Direct threats have greatly diminished but not completely withdrawn, especially in respect of new roads. The consequences of ceasing traditional uses and placing the heaths within the context of urban development are considerable. However, the rarity of the habitat and the scarcity of many of the species which depend upon it clearly dictates that these difficulties must be addressed. Furthermore no other habitat satisfies so well our own need to escape to and enjoy at least a taste of the wilderness once so freely available to our forefathers. Surely we owe it to ourselves to ensure that the heaths can continue to delight our eyes – and those of generations to come.

CONSERVING THE HEATHS

PROTECTING THE HEATH

Sites judged by this country's statutory nature conservation body, English Nature (formerly the Nature Conservancy Council) to be of outstanding importance for nature conservation are designated as Sites of Special Scientific Interest (SSSIs). Not altogether surprisingly the majority of heathland in Dorset (some 90% of the total area) is now so designated. On top of this, European designations are also in place with almost all of the SSSIs additionally being Special Protection Areas (SPAs) by virtue of their special bird interest, and most additionally being candidate Special Areas for Conservation (SACs) by virtue of their special plant communities. Most heaths are also Ramsar sites, by virtue of being internationally important wetlands. The small areas of heath which are not SSSIs are recognised as Sites of Nature Conservation Interest (SNCIs), a designation created to recognise sites which are of at least county importance to wildlife.

Heathland habitat is now protected by a number of special designations. Some of its rarest species are given additional protection. The ladybird spider (*Eresus cinnaberinus*), having only one known surviving location in the United Kingdom – in Dorset, is one such species.

Clay diggers at Mitchell's Brickworks in Parkstone (Poole) in 1920.
They left behind a lake which is now the centrepiece of Alder Hills Nature
Reserve – shown on the opposite page.

All these initials may seem very complex, but they add up to a very
simple message – Dorset heathland is no longer up for grabs – and
they give the planners the critical tool which they need to resist any
remaining misplaced ambitions to develop them. They should also
provide a tool to resist development too close to them, for as we have
seen, heathland and its wildlife is very vulnerable when placed within
or immediately adjacent to housing. All these initials feature strongly
in statutory development plans which decide what will, and will not,
be allowed where. Even in the cases where the initials might have
seemed to have arrived too late – in the case of old consents for
mineral winning or long standing plans for new roads for example –
the piling of so many accolades on top of the heath might yet protect
it! Further loss to farming and forestry is very much a thing of the
past, although the replanting of harvested conifer plantations just as
they are returning to heathland is a sad disappointment.

But holding back the tide of direct loss – hard enough as that may
be at times – is only a part of the need. We must then care for that
which we have saved. Much heathland, a little over half of the total in
fact, is now in some form of nature reserve cared for by one or other
of the several bodies concerned with heathland conservation in
Dorset. English Nature declared its first National Nature Reserve at

Alder Hills Nature Reserve, a protected haven, managed by the Dorset Wildlife Trust, in the heart of Poole.

Hartland Moor near Corfe Castle in 1954 and went on to dedicate several more, including Studland, Godlingston and Holt Heaths – for which we have the Bankes Estate's gift to the National Trust to be eternally grateful for. The RSPB has extended determinedly inland from its original holding on the Arne peninsula, not just for the benefit of birds but for all heathland wildlife. Similarly the Herpetological Conservation Trust, while highlighting concern for reptiles and amphibians in its name, inevitably takes on the care of other wildlife within its reserves. The Dorset Wildlife Trust has built up an impressive portfolio of heathland reserves from the very small, such as Alder Hills hidden in the heart of Poole, to the more extensive, such as Tadnoll (*see illustration on page 11*) and Winfrith. Our Local Authorities also hold land with nature conservation as a priority and such heathland sites may now be found from Stephens Castle at

Verwood to Ham Common and Bourne Valley in Poole to Town Common at Christchurch, while in the centre of the triangle lies Avon Heath Country Park. Some are declared as Local Nature Reserves.

But not all heathland either could (or arguably should need to be) formally dedicated as nature reserves. Some private owners may wish to care for it directly themselves, and some public owners, such as the Forestry Commission and the MOD, must do so as a part of their own particular primary functions. The vital thing is that, be it within or without of a nature reserve, the heath is positively managed.

MANAGING THE HEATH

We have seen how man's activities led to the formation of the heaths in the Bronze Age and how his subsequent treatment of them maintained their open nature, imposed diversity of age structure upon them and created numerous special habitats within them. As a result the heath was maintained, and its rare and specialised wildlife flourished. Then we saw how the heathland not only diminished and fragmented, but outlived its traditional functions, with the result that not only was diversity and rarity threatened, but the habitat itself was lost by progressive takeover by trees. So to keep Dorset heathland in the manner to which it became accustomed (and richly deserves) we have either to re-establish those traditional uses or to simulate them via modern methods.

Removing the backlog of tree and scrub encroachment from the heath is often a vital first step – and one which sometimes causes public concern. We forget, or do not realise, that only a generation or two ago the heaths were largely treeless and we may thus see the removal of trees as an unnatural and unwelcome change! But once achieved, the restoration to heath is usually accepted and appreciated – especially when one is so quickly rewarded by the sight of a basking sand lizard on a tree stump. And some native trees are always left for character – and future generations of hobbies. No such mercy should be shown to the alien Rhododendron and American Crowberry however, for their wildlife value is minimal, and that which is spared has no hesitation in spreading again its deadly mantle – creating more work for the future. Bracken too, no longer pulled up for bedding,

Scrub and trees are a part of the heathland scene, as here on Canford
Heath, but in recent years they have over-extended their welcome.

may have smothered extensive areas and must be deterred.

Once the heath has re-emerged into the sunshine, plans for
ongoing management can be made. Rejuvenating the heath on a
cyclical basis to deplete nutrients, prevent future scrub encroachment,
and ensure a variable age structure is a key consideration. In certain
circumstances this can be done by carefully controlled, small scale
light winter burning, or, where the terrain permits, by mechanical
cutting. More recently there has been a move towards the return of
low intensity grazing which, apart from installing a more sustainable
management regime, links to a past where grazing was normal and
potentially steps forward to meet the demand for organic produce.
Grazing animals will help to keep the vegetation open and create
some bare ground, especially on the wetter areas where sundews and

Volunteer working party cutting gorse at the Dorset Wildlife Trust's
Higher Hyde Heath Nature Reserve

marsh gentians may thrive on exposed peat, but some mechanical
help may also be needed, especially for the provision of sand on dry
slopes where stock is less likely to wander (and may in any event be
unwelcome in the delicate environs where sand lizards lay their eggs
or hunting wasps dig their burrows).

Cutting common gorse is another traditional practice which
heathland managers now organise, not as in the past to provide fuel,
but to ensure that resprouted vigorous gorse is always available as a
source of invertebrates and nesting sites for birds – especially the
Dartford warbler. Sometimes controlled winter burning of gorse is
used as an alternative method of rejuvenation – and any conservation
volunteer who has experienced the delights of gorse cutting will tell
you why!

Another specialist home on the heath which is no longer ensured by
traditional activities is water. So today we deliberately dig ponds and
maintain ditches especially for bladderwort, dragonflies, damselflies
and raft spiders. We also do it to provide a water source for fire
fighting. Fire prevention and control is a major consideration in
heathland management, especially on those urban heaths which tend
to suffer so badly from fire. All heaths need special fire plans providing
good access for fire fighting vehicles, fire breaks, fire beaters, and of
course water sources – hydrants or ponds. And just as fire ponds may

The beautiful pale heath violet (*Viola lactea*) is naturally restricted to heaths in the south and south-west of England and parts of the Welsh coast. On its heathland locations it needs open grassy conditions and has declined significantly in recent years. In Dorset, only some eight sites are still known. On Higher Hyde Heath active intervention by the Dorset Wildlife Trust to prevent scrub encroachment and provide open ground is enabling it to thrive.

be dual purpose, 'mobile' mown firebreaks can also serve to rejuvenate heather while ploughed breaks, or ploughed edges to mown breaks, can provide that vital open sand resource. Integration is the key!

PUTTING THE CLOCK BACK

'You cannot put the clock back.' Well sometimes we should certainly try – and indeed sometimes perhaps we can!

Provided the ground has not been sterilised by development or the soil not irretrievably enriched, heathland can be encouraged to return from former agriculture or forestry. Return from forestry undoubtedly offers the greatest potential with substantial areas of conifer plantation on former heathland falling due for clear felling within the next decade or so. Welcome, but relatively modest, concessions by the Forestry Commission have shown that simply left alone such cleared areas readily revert to heath. If treated correctly, some sites may offer the possibility of heathland creation from scratch – such as on top of restored modern mineral workings. Seed bearing heather cut or 'harvested' from one heath as part of a rejuvenation and firebreaking programme may be used to create another.

By these means it is possible to extend existing heathlands – and even to reconnect previously divided sites. This has enormous benefits as larger continuous areas are more diverse, easier to manage and more robust – less vulnerable to decline and localised extinctions. The first moves towards putting the clock back were of a small scale and experimental nature but as more has been learnt and the importance of trying more fully recognised, so larger scale practical exercises have been undertaken with every prospect of real success. Sometimes careful reintroduction of species into restored or re-established heathland may be feasible.

WORKING TOGETHER FOR HEATHLAND

Working to conserve heathland and its wildlife is thus no mean task. It requires enormous determination in the face of ongoing pressure. It requires significant funding – sometimes the buying or leasing of land is necessary, but always the management of it is vital and this also

Hartland Moor, declared in 1954, was Dorset's first National Nature Reserve. Today it is the central jewel within an extensive reserve mosaic, much of which has been actively re-established as heathland out of farmland or forestry. Grazing animals again wander the heath. Several nature conservation bodies work together to manage this national asset and provide the public with access and information.

A young natterjack toad (*Bufo calamita*), identified by the pale stripe down its back. Natterjacks have recently been successfully re-introduced to some of their former sites in Dorset.

costs money. Machinery is needed, specific chemicals sometimes must be applied, and for even sustainable grazing management there are the high initial costs of fencing, cattle-gridding and stocking. A sizeable workforce is now employed in caring for the heaths. Help with funding has been available for some time through English Nature, who run several schemes to aid heathland management. Recently this support has been substantially increased by the injection of funds from the Heritage Lottery. Another recent development is the dedication of funds from European sources, not just for managing the vegetation, but also for combatting the problems arising from urban pressure. However, grants must usually be matched by the recipient's own contributions and these are hard to come by. English Nature cannot be expected to fund its fellow government agencies and, with the MOD owning some 20% of heathland in Dorset and the Forestry Commission owning 6% (but potentially much more), these bodies need substantial budgets dedicated to meeting their responsibliies for heathland management.

Working to conserve heathland especially involves close and continuing co-operation between many diverse bodies from our national government, local councils, English Nature, voluntary conservation bodies, fire and police services, and private and public landowners. Finally it involves a commitment from you and me.

When we go to the heath we need to ensure that we are aware of and respect its needs. It is important to follow the 'heathland code' keeping to the well-worn paths so as to avoid making new ones, keeping dogs under control especially during the bird breeding season and making use of dog bins. It is, of course, vital never to risk starting a fire by discarded matches, cigarettes or broken bottles. There is now often the opportunity to join the local 'Heath Watch' – volunteers who act as wardens, deterring mountain bikers and motor cyclists and reporting problems to whoever is formally responsible. This idea was pioneered on Canford Heath and has been copied elsewhere with encouraging results. There is also much satisfaction to be had in joining a volunteer 'working party' and helping directly to manage a heath! Simply becoming a member of a voluntary conservation body such as the Dorset Wildlife Trust supports their endeavours in all aspects of heathland conservation. We can all help to ensure that Dorset heathland is always available to delight the eyes of anybody prepared simply to take a proper look!

Rainbarrow in the late nineteenth century, from where, in Thomas Hardy's *Return of the Native*, Eustacia Vye gazed out over the open expanse of Egdon Heath. Since then Rainbarrow has been hidden by forest and scrub, but it may yet again rise above glorious open heathland.

VISITING THE HEATHS

Walking the heaths enables one to capture the atmosphere of this historic Dorset landscape, so closely associated wit'ı Thomas Hardy, and to enjoy the wildlife it supports.You can observe how much has been taken for housing, industry, mineral working, forestry and farming, and appreciate at first hand the challenges which confront the conservation bodies trying to restore some of its former glory.

KEY: BBC: Bournemouth Borough Council; CBC: Christchurch Borough Council; DCC: Dorset County Council; DWT: Dorset Wildlife Trust; EDDC: East Dorset District Council; EN: English Nature; FE: Forest Enterprise; HCT: Herpetological Conservation Trust; NT: National Trust; PBC: Poole Borough Council; RSPB: Royal Society for the Protection of Birds.

Many of these organisations conduct guided walks and other events on their heaths. See the 'greenlink' guide published bi-annually.

AFFPUDDLE AND BRYANTSPUDDLE HEATHS, BERE REGIS (SW 810920) [FE]. Coniferous woodland interspersed with areas of open heath and bog. Well-marked tracks for walkers. Parking at Affpuddle (SW 805925) and Cull-peppers Dish (SW 815925).

ALDER HILLS, POOLE (SZ 063931) [DWT]. 5 hectare Local Nature Reserve comprising a large lake, formerly a clay pit, a margin of carr woodland and slopes and ridges of dry heathland. Parking and main access at Talbot View Community Centre next to Sainsburys, 4 Alder Park, off Alder Road, Parkstone (SZ 063933).

ARNE, WAREHAM (SY 973881) [RSPB]. Varied 500 hectare nature reserve with extensive heathland, woodland and marshes bordering Poole Harbour. Footpath to Shipstal Point open all year; trail to Middebere open in winter. Hides. Parking at RSPB car park only at reserve entrance near Arne village (SY 923972).

AVON HEATH COUNTRY PARK, RINGWOOD (SU 125039) [DCC/RSPB]. Large country park comprising mainly dry heathland and conifer woods. Separate sections (North Park, Matchams View, South Park) totalling 243 hectares. Visitor Centre, events, activities for children, picnic sites and waymarked paths. Car park for North Park and Visitor Centre off south side of A31 roundabout by

St. Leonards Hotel (SU 122029). Car parks for Matchams View off Hurn Lane (SU134021) and for South Park off Boundary Lane (SU 127023).

BLUE POOL, FURZEBROOK, WAREHAM (SY 935834). Attractive pool, formerly a clay pit, with surrounding heathland. Open March-Nov inclusive, with admission charge. Refreshments, guidebook. Private car park for Blue Pool visitors only.

BOURNE VALLEY AND TALBOT HEATH, POOLE (SZ 070930) [PBC]. Local Nature Reserve comprising wet and dry heath bisected by the Bourne Stream. A good example of an urban heathland open space providing recreational and excellent educational opportunities to residents and schools. Network of footpaths. Access off Alder Road at end of Winston Avenue near Talbot Combined School.

BROWNSEA ISLAND, POOLE (SZ 025882) [NT]. Small heathland area on south side of Island near Baden Powell Memorial. Island open from late March to October. Boats from Poole Quay and Sandbanks. Landing fee. Reception Centre, shop and cafe at Quay. Boat cruises round the Harbour offer fine views of the extensive Studland and Godlingston Heaths to the south.

CANFORD HEATH, POOLE (SZ 030955) [PBC]. Extensive mainly dry heathland adjoining Poole & Broadstone. Illustrates the challenge of conserving heathland close to a large built-up area. Access from end of Francis Avenue off roundabout at junction of Wallisdown Rd (A3049) and Ringwood Rd (A348) (SZ 46952) or from lay-by (near AA Box) on Gravel Hill (A349) (SZ 015956).

COOMBE HEATH, LULWORTH (SY 861847) [DWT]. 40 hectares comprising dry heath with barrows rising from wet heath and bog. Access by bridle paths and a permissive path. Very limited parking at SY 859849.

CORFE AND BARROW HILLS, BROADSTONE (SZ005973) [PBC]. 2 units of mainly dry and some wet heath, north of Broadstone. Access to Corfe Hills from Higher Blandford Road (B3074) at SY 999966 and Barrow Hills from Merley Park Road at SY 999979. Limited Parking.

CRANBORNE COMMON, ALDERHOLT (SU 108118) [DWT]. 45 hectare reserve of mainly humid and wet heath. Use public bridleway from Verwood (by Stephens Castle SU 090098 see entry below) north to Alderholt.

CREECH HEATH, WAREHAM (SY 925840) [HCT]. Large heathland with old clay workings situated between the Grange Road and Furzebrook Road south of Wareham. Access from Icen Barrow Gate on Grange Road (SY918839).

DEWLANDS COMMON, VERWOOD (SU 077083) [EDDC]. 13 hectare dry heathland Local Nature Reserve between Verwood and the River Crane. Access from Dewlands Road.

DUNYEATS HILL, BROADSTONE (SZ 013965) [HCT]. Modest reserve of dry and wet heath south of, and continuous with Delph Woods [PBC]. Car Park in Delph Woods off Gravel Hill (A349) at SZ 016976 or from Gravel Hill direct at SZ 016969 or Moorfie'us Ave at SZ 012966.

EBBLAKE BOG, VERWOOD (SU 105071) [FE]. 13 hectares of bog and marginal wet heath on w. edge of Ringwood Forest north of Moors Valley Country Park. Other heathland remnants in the wider forest area. Limited parking off B3081 at SU 109078 with access via forest track southwards, or at Moors Valley Country Park via forest track northwards: charged car park at SU 104054 with access.

FERNDOWN COMMON, FERNDOWN (SZ 998068) [HCT]. 65 hectares of mainly dry heath west of Ferndown. Barrows and ponds. Car park off Wimborne Road East at SZ 066008.

GODLINGSTON HEATH, SWANAGE (see also STUDLAND HEATH) (SZ 015825) [NT]. Large expanse of varied and undulating heathland overlooking Poole Harbour and featuring the Agglestone rock. Contiguous with Studland Heath on the sea side of the Ferry Road and managed as a single National Nature Reserve. Access from lay-by on Ferry Road, Studland at head of track to Greenlands Farm (SZ 026843) or from Dean Hill just east of Purbeck Golf Club (SZ 016819).

GOLDEN CAP, CHIDEOCK (SY 405922) [NT]. An example of heathland developed on a greensand coastal hilltop in West Dorset. Dry heath with high proportion of bracken. Access on foot from Seatown (SY 421918) or from car park off A35 (SY 412933) via Langdon Hill.

GREAT OVENS HILL, WAREHAM (SY 927904) [HCT]. Dry and wet heath on southern edge of Wareham Forest and immediately north of Sandford. Access from B3075 road. Small walkers' car parks nearby.

HAM COMMON, POOLE (SY 982908) [PBC]. Local Nature Reserve on shore of Poole Harbour adjoining Rockley Park. The Reserve features a large flooded former clay working – Hamworthy Lake. Fine views over Poole Harbour to Arne. Access from Rockley viewpoint car park at end of Napier Avenue by entrance to caravan park. Alternative parking by the beach off Lake Drive nearby.

HARDY'S MONUMENT, DORCHESTER (SY 613877) [NT/PRIVATE]. Dry heathland on a prominent ridge just beyond the Poole Basin S.W. of Dorchester. Car Park by monument.

HARTLAND MOOR/STOBOROUGH HEATH, WAREHAM (SY 945855) [NT/EN]. One of the largest and first nature reserves in Dorset, Hartland Moor National Nature Reserve of 741 hectares has been supplemented in recent years by an extension onto Stoborough Heath. Superb dry heathland and valley bog draining into Poole Harbour. Paths include old mineral tramway with hides. Areas of heathland restoration adjoin (Langton Wallis, New Mills etc). Access from car park at 'Sunnyside' on Arne road (SY 937863) or pull in on Arne/Corfe road at Middlebere (SY 963854).

HENGISTBURY HEAD, BOURNEMOUTH (SZ 175907) [BBC]. 100 hectare coastal heath on eastern edge of Bournemouth. Overlooks both the sea and Christchurch Harbour. Visitor Centre. Car park and foot access at end of Broadway off Belle Vue Road, Southbourne (SZ 166912).

HIGHER HYDE HEATH, WAREHAM (SY 851902) [DWT]. 54 hectare reserve including dry and wet heath, bog and wet woodland. Hide and car park off Wareham-Puddletown road near Hanson offices south-east of Gallows Hill (SY 854897).

HOLT HEATH, WIMBORNE (SU 060040) [NT/EN]. Magnificent expanse (411 hectares) of heath north east of Wimborne encompassing dry and wet heath and bog. Designated a National Nature Reserve. Also a registered common with rights still existing for grazing and collection of wood. Bridleways and footpaths criss-cross the heath. Limited parking on minor road from Holt to Three-Legged Cross (Summerlug Hill) and at White Sheet Hill car park (048037).

HURN FOREST HEATHS, CHRISTCHURCH (SU 104015 and SZ 135991) [FE]. Heathland and bog fragments within Hurn Forest plantations. Forest paths provide access. Access from Matcham's Lane car park north of Hurn village at SZ 128989, or from Boundary Lane car park at SZ 104023.

HYDE BOG, WAREHAM (SY 875918) [FE]. Large bog with marginal wet and dry heath within Wareham Forest, north of Wareham. Other heathland remnants in the wider forest area. Access by forest paths near Stroud Bridge (SY 889914).

LIONS HILL, ST LEONARDS (SU 106040) [HCT]. 43 hectares of dry and wet heath and bog immediately east of the Moors River. Access via Lions Lane (roadside parking only) at SU106039.

MORDEN BOG, WAREHAM (SY 915910) [EN]. 149 hectare National Nature Reserve within Wareham Forest (FE) north of Wareham. Dry heathland and one of the largest valley bogs in England, with duck decoy ponds. Other heathland fragments within wider Forest. Access by forest paths from Sherford Bridge (SY 919927) on B3075 Morden road north of Sandford and from main Forest Car Park off Wareham-Bere Regis road (start of Sika deer trail, SY 906893).

PARLEY COMMON, WEST PARLEY (SZ 090990) [HCT]. 168 hectares of dry and wet heath lying east of the Ferndown/Parley conurbation. Access via Barrack Road off B3073 at SZ 094979 or Lone Pine Drive at SZ 086991.

PUDDLETOWN HEATH, DORCHESTER (SY 740930) [DCC & FE]. Coniferous forest interspersed with heathland remnants. Waymarked walks. Access via Thorncombe Wood from car park near Hardy's Cottage, Higher Bockhampton – south of the A35 (SY 726922).

SANDFORD HEATH, WAREHAM (SY 940902) [EN]. Block of varied heath between railway line and A351. Access via footpath off Black Hill Road (SY 943903) 2 minute walk from Holton Heath Railway Station.

SLOP BOG, WEST MOORS (SU 077018) [DCC]. Old peat cuttings still visible on this 20 hectare bog system with surrounding wet, but very little dry, heath. Boardwalk over bog. Access via footpath from West Moors Road (B3072) at SU080017 or Redwood Drive at SU 074017.

SOPLEY COMMON AND RAMSDOWN, HURN (SZ 132975) [DWT/HCT]. 33 hectare dry and wet heathland reserve and registered common. Parking in lay-by opposite garden nursery at SZ 129971 near Hurn village. Continuous southwards with Ramsdown Hill.

STEPHENS CASTLE, VERWOOD (SU 092095) [EDDC]. Local nature reserve of over 23 hectares of heath. Central part formerly a sand and gravel quarry. Hilltop barrow and viewpoint. Wet areas, ponds and scrub/woodland. Foot access from St. Stephens Lane (SY 097093), Vicarage Road (SY 088093) and Coopers Lane (SY 090098) off B3081 Ringwood-Cranborne road in Verwood.

STUDLAND HEATH, SWANAGE (SZ 030845) [NT]. Part of a large coastal National Nature Reserve which continues on west side of Ferry Road as Godlingston Heath (see entry above). Heathland and dunes surround the Little Sea freshwater lake behind the sands of Studland Bay. Illustrates the succession of vegetation from the embryo sand dunes adjoining the beach, through a series of dune heath ridges to the mature stable heathland by the Ferry Road. Nature trails, visitor and education centres, refreshments, observation hides, guided walks etc. Main NT car parks at Knoll Beach (SZ 033835) and Shell Bay (SZ 035862). Limited parking at Greenland Farm turning (SZ 025843).

TADNOLL (see also WINFRITH HEATH) (SY 792873) [DWT]. 44 hectare reserve of mainly dry heathland and wet meadowland on western edge of Winfrith Heath. Limited parking on roadside at reserve entrance at SY 792873. Access by permissive path.

TOWN COMMON AND ST. CATHERINE'S HILL, CHRISTCHURCH (SZ 138996) [CBC/HCT]. At 257 hectares, one of our most extensive tracts of dry and wet heathland with pools. Outstanding views over the Avon Valley from St Catherine's Hill. Car park off Fairmile (B3073) at SZ 146946.

TURBARY COMMON, BOURNEMOUTH (SZ 060945) [BBC]. Heathland remnant demonstrating challenge of conserving heathland in urban environment. Access from Turbary Park Avenue.

TURNERSPUDDLE HEATH, WAREHAM (SY 824912) [DCC]. Small triangular open heath area between MOD danger area and FE conifer plantations. Bridle path north from cross-roads by Clouds Hill (Lawrence of Arabia cottage NT).

UPTON HEATH, POOLE (SY 9899510 [DWT]. Large urban heathland reserve close to Poole, overlooking Harbour. Fascinating mosaic of dry, humid and wet heath, bog pools etc. Like Canford Heath (see separate entry earlier) it illustrates the management challenges of maintaining quality heathland close to housing development. Access from end of Beacon Road, Broadstone (SY 989952) or car park off Springdale Road, Corfe Mullen (SY 986958).

WINFRITH HEATH, WOOL (see also TADNOLL) (SY 805870) [DWT]. Large varied heath west of Winfrith Technology Centre (formerly UKAEA). Access from Gatemoor Lane (Blacknoll) north of A352 opposite Red Lion at Winfrith Newburgh.

WOOLS BARROW, WAREHAM (SY 094926) [FE]. Dry heathland clothing Iron Age hillfort with views over Wareham Forest. Other heathland remnants and connected to Morden Bog (see separate entry) through forest tracks. Access via Stroud Bridge at SY 889914.

FURTHER READING

Bibby, C.J., *Conservation of the Dartford Warbler on English lowland heaths*. (Biological Conservation 13 299-307), 1978

Byfield, A.J. & Pearman, D., *Dorset's disappearing heathland flora* (Plantlife, London/RSPB, Sandy), 1994

Claridge, J., *General View of the County of Dorset* (W. Smith, London), 1793

Cunningham, G.L., *The Changing Landscape of the Dorset Heathlands 1750-1950* (PhD. Thesis Univ. Lond), 1974

Defoe, D., *A tour through the whole Island of Great Britain* (Mr. P. Davies Bol 1 205-210), 1724

Dimbleby, G.W., *The development of British Heathlands and their Soils* (Oxford For. Mem 23 1-121), 1962

Dorset Heathland Forum, *Dorset Heathland Strategy* (Dorset County Council), 1990

Dorset Wildlife Trust, *The Natural History of Dorset* (Dovecote Press), 1997

Farrell, L. (ed), *Focus on Nature Conservation No 2 Heathland Management* (Shrewsbury Nature Conservancy Council)

Gimmingham, C., *Ecology of Heathlands* (Chapman and Hall), 1972

Goddard, P.F., *Morphology, growth, food, habits and population characteristics of the Smooth Snake Coronella austriaca in southern Britain* (J. Zool., Lond. 204. 241-257), 1984

Godwin, *The Origin of the British Flora* (Cambridge: Cambridge University Press), 1975

Good, R., *A Geographical Handbook of the Dorset Flora* (Dorset Natural Hist. & Arch. Soc., Dorchester), 1948

Grinsell, L.V., *Dorset Barrows* (Longmans, Dorchester), 1959

Hardy, T., *The Return of the Native* (McMillan, Lond), 1878

Haskins, L.E., *The Vegetational History of South-east Dorset* (PhD. Thesis. University of Southampton)

Haskins, L.E., *Heathlands in an Urban Setting – effects of urban development on heathlands of south-east Dorset* (British Wildlife 11 299-237), 2000

Hutchins, J., *The History and Antiquities of the County of Dorset* (1774)

Kerr, B.V., *Bound to the Soil. A Social History of Dorset* (Wakefield. EP Publishing), 1968

Mahon, A. & Pearman, D., *Endangered Wildlife in Dorset.* (The county Red Data Book. Dorset Environmental Records Centre), 1993

Merrett, P., *The Phenology of Spiders on Heathland in Dorset* (J. Ecol. 50 369-391), 1967

Moore, N.W., *The heaths of Dorset and their conservation* (J. Ecol. 50. 369-91), 1962

Moulton, N. & Corbett, K., *The Sand Lizard Conservation Handbook* (English Nature), 1999

Mountford, Brian M., Abbot, A. & Vincent S., *The changes in ant species distribution during ten years post-fire generation of a heath* (J. Anim. Ecol. 45 115-33), 1976

Nicholson, A.M., *The ecology of the Sand Lizard* (Lacerta agilis) *in southern England and comparisons with the Common Lizard* (L. Vivipara) (PhD. Thesis, University of Southampton), 1980

Pennington, W., *The History of the British Vegetation* (London English Universities Press), 1969

Rose, R., Webb, N., Clarke R. & Traynor, C., *Changes on the Heathland in Dorset England between 1987 & 1996* (Biol Con 93 117-125), 2000

Spellerberg I.F. & Phelps, T.E., *Biology, general ecology and behaviour of the snake* Coronella austriaca Laurenti (biol J. Linn. Soc. 9. 158-6, 4), 1977

Stewart, A., Pearman, D. & Preston, C., *Scarce Plants in Britain* (JNCC Peterborough), 1994

Symes, N. & Day, J., *The Lowland Heath Management Handbook* (RSPB Publications. In press)

Webb, N., *Heathlands* (The New Naturalist Library. Collins), 1986

Webb, N.R., *Changes on the heathlands of Dorset, England, between 1978 & 1987* (Biol. Cons. 51 273-286), 1987

Webb, N. & Haskins L.E., *An ecological survey of heathland in the Poole Basin, Dorset, England in 1978* (Biol Cons. 17 281-96), 1980

Webb, N.R. and Hopkins, P.J., *Invertebrate diversity on fragmented calluna -heathland* (J. app. Ecol. 21. 921-33), 1984

Wigginton, M., *British Red Data Books 1 Vascular plants.* 3rd Ed. (JNCC Peterborough), 1999

Young, A., *The farmers tour through the east of England* (Letters XXV1 & XXV11, 245-325), 1771

ACKNOWLEDGEMENTS

The idea of writing about the wildlife of Dorset, firstly in a single book, and then through the Discovering Dorset series was that of Tony Bates, Chairman of the Dorset Wildlife Trust. I am grateful to him for this idea and particularly for his invitation to write about the heathlands. Tony has cheerfully steered the whole project.

I am greatly indebted to many scientists and conservationists whom I have met and worked with over the years, initially at Furzebrook Research Station and then additionally with English Nature, (formerly the Nature Conservancy Council), the RSPB, the Herpetological Conservation Trust and the Dorset Wildlife Trust. It is they who have done the work and had the knowledge, they who willingly passed it on, and they who have inspired and encouraged me to make use of it over the years and ultimately in this book. Space allows only specific mention of a very few of them; Steve Chapman who patiently guided my historical studies of the heaths, Nigel Webb whose surveys permitted me the privilege of walking them, Helen Brotherton who invited me to work to protect them, and Eve Dennis and Jim White who welcomed my efforts to help them do it.

I am very grateful to the many determined people who have done so much recently to increase the scale of heathland conservation taking place in Dorset and thus provide me with a happily positive perspective to write from. In addition to the staff of English Nature these particularly include Keith Corbett, Stan Davis and Martin Auld (and his successors in the RSPB heathland project) and Phil Sterling.

Jamie McMillan and Andrew Nicholson have provided welcome advice and constant enouragement.

Bill Copland has kindly prepared the 'Visiting the Heaths' gazetteer and proofed the text.

I am grateful to Nigel Symes of the RSPB Dorset Heathland Project for providing the heathland distribution map for 1997 and Christopher Chaplin for the map on page 7.

I would like to thank the following for allowing the inclusion of illustrations in their possession or which they hold the copyright: Tony Bates; front cover, pages 4 (left), 11, 25, 28, 31, 32, 33, 40, 48 (bottom), 49 (bottom), 56, 62, 63: Denny Cook; back cover: Robert Dickson (Natural Image); page 54: Dorset County Museum; pages 12, 48 (top), 67: Dorset

Wildlife Trust; page 53: The Dovecote Press; page 14: David Element (Natural Image); pages 29 (left), 37 (top): Bob Gibbons; frontispiece, pages 4 (right), 8, 15, 16, 17, 18, 19, 20, 21 (both), 22, 23, 24 (all), 26, 27, 29 (right), 30, 34, 39, 51 (top), 59, 61, 65 (both), 66 : Paul Harris; page 37 (bottom): Graham Hatherley, BBC Natural History Unit; page 55: Phil Sterling; page 57: Colin Varndell; pages 35, 36, 41, 43, 44, 50: Peter Wilson, Natural Image; page 51 (bottom): Poole Museum Service; pages 49 (top), 58.

INDEX

The

DISCOVER DORSET

Series of Books include

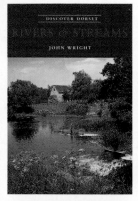

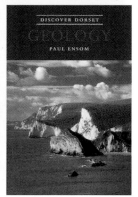

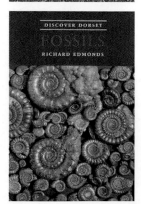

All the books about Dorset published by
The Dovecote Press
are available in bookshops throughout the
county, or in case of difficulty direct from the
publishers.
The Dovecote Press Ltd, Stanbridge,
Wimborne, Dorset BH21 4JD
Tel: 01258 840549
www.dovecotepress.com